TEAM BRASS

Trumpet/Cornet

RICHARD DUCKETT

**Edited by William Rumford, Philip Evry
and Geoffry Russell-Smith**

First published in 1988 by International Music Publications Ltd
This edition © 2007 by Faber Music Ltd
This edition first published in 2007 by Faber Music Ltd
Bloomsbury House 74–77 Great Russell Street London WC1B 3DA
Cover photography by Keven Erickson
Cover design by Susan Clarke
Instruments photographed by kind permission of Yamaha-Kemble Music (UK) Ltd
Typeset by Cromwell Typesetting & Design Ltd, London
Printed in England by Caligraving Ltd

ISBN10: 0-571-52817-1
EAN13: 978-0-571-52817-2

To buy Faber Music publications or to find out about the full range of titles
available please contact your local music retailer or Faber Music sales enquiries:
Faber Music Ltd, Burnt Mill, Elizabeth Way, Harlow CM20 2HX
Tel: +44 (0) 1279 82 89 82   Fax: +44 (0) 1279 82 89 83
sales@fabermusic.com   fabermusic.com

The author is donating a percentage of his royalties from **Team Brass**
to a children's charity

FABER *ff* MUSIC

For Mary

Introduction

The *Team Brass* series has been designed to meet the needs of young brass musicians everywhere, whether lessons are given individually, in groups or in the classroom.

Musical variety

Each book contains a wide range of musical styles, from the Baroque and Classical eras to film, folk, jazz and Latin American. In addition there are original pieces and studies, technical exercises and scales, progressing from the beginner stage to approximately Grade 4 standard. Furthermore *Team Brass* offers material suitable for mixed brass ensemble as well as solos with piano accompaniment (see following page for further details).

CD

The accompanying free CD contains over 75 digital backing tracks for individual and group use. See page iv for a complete track listing.

Progression

The *Team Brass* series is not a 'method', rather a collection of music from which the teacher can select a suitably graded course for each pupil. This allows for variation in starting-point, concentration threshold and pace of progression. There is a choice of starting notes and several choices of progressive path the pupil can follow. Study options appear at the foot of most pages.

General musicianship skills

In addition to fostering musical literacy, *Rhythm Grids*, *Letter-name Grids* and *Play by Ear* lines provide early opportunities for composition and improvisation. Comprehensive notes on the use of this series, scores of ensemble pieces, piano accompaniments and approaches to creative music-making are given in the *Team Brass Piano Accompaniments* book (0-571-52821-X).

Acknowledgements

Sincere thanks are extended to the following people whose criticism, advice and help in various ways has been invaluable: Keith Allen, Colin Moore, Brian Wicks, Keith Watts, Peter Smalley, Molly Wicks and Philip Leah, whose enthusiasm and support have been a great encouragement.

Team Brass ensemble

The ensemble material in *Team Brass* has been specially written so that it can be played by almost any combination of brass instruments: there are a wide range of ensemble options to experiment with which are explained below. *Team Brass* can also be integrated with *Team Woodwind* and *Team Strings*, which will enable you to cater for almost any combination of instruments up to full orchestra, or to use the pieces in a classroom setting. All *Team* ensemble parts are carefully graded to correspond to the introduction of solo tuition material throughout each tutor. Much of the *Team* ensemble material now plays a prominent part in the Music Medals syllabus of the ABRSM.

Duets for trumpet

Team Brass includes 17 duets for trumpet:

German tune	*page 14*	Brass group warm-up 2	*page 38*
Lullaby	*page 14*	Tijuana brass	*page 39*
Canzonetta	*page 15*	I saw three ships	*page 39*
Brass group warm-up 1	*page 19*	Michael row the boat	*page 48*
Regal fanfare	*page 20*	Canzona	*page 48*
When I first came to this land	*page 20*	O Little Town of Bethlehem	*page 49*
Blowin' in the wind	*page 21*	St Anthony Chorale	*page 49*
Au clair de la lune	*page 37*	March from Judas Maccabaeus	*page 55*
Little donkey	*page 37*		

Creating brass trios and quartets

All of these duets are marked with this logo to indicate they can be expanded into brass trios or quartets by adding inessential and independent third and fourth parts for other instruments.

- second and third parts appear in the French Horn book (0-571-52818-X)
- fourth parts appear in the Trombone/Euphonium book (bass clef) (0-571-52819-8)
- third and fourth parts for treble clef brass band instruments are provided as supplements available for free download from fabermusic.com.
- The ⊞ pieces appear on the **same numbered page** in each book, i.e. *Canzonetta* is on page 15 in all books.

Integrating with *Team Woodwind*

The ⊞ ensemble pieces in *Team Brass* can also be integrated with those pieces (on the same pages) in *Team Woodwind*. By combining all the ensemble parts in *Team Brass* and *Team Woodwind* you can form a full-sized wind band, with either the brass or woodwind taking the lead.

Integrating with *Team Strings*

Additionally, *Team Strings* can be integrated with *Team Woodwind* and *Team Brass* by using the supplementary parts to the ⊞ ensemble pieces that can be downloaded from fabermusic.com. This allows for almost any combination of instruments up to full orchestra, or in a classroom setting.

Piano accompaniments

This logo indicates which pieces have a piano accompaniment. Scores for all ensemble material and more extensive notes are also included in the *Team Brass Piano Accompaniments* book (0-571-52821-X).

NB Because the ensemble pieces produce a starting point for players at various stages of development, these may include technical elements (new notes, rhythms etc.) that are not introduced until some pages later.

CD track listing

Some tracks work with two different tunes.
Each track includes two bars of clicks to bring you in.

CD tracks orchestrated by Gordon Watts

Production: Mark Mumford

Track 29 published by Chappell Music Ltd

Tracks 8 & 55 published by Warner Chappell Music Ltd

All other tracks ℗ and © 1994 International Music Publications Ltd

Lesson diary & practice chart

Date (week commencing)	Enter number of minutes practised.							Teacher indicates which pages to study.
	Mon	Tue	Wed	Thur	Fri	Sat	Sun	
	Mon	Tue	Wed	Thur	Fri	Sat	Sun	

Getting started

Teachers, who like pupils to experiment with the instrument before learning to use the text, can write helpful notes below, according to the needs of the student.*

Otherwise proceed as follows:
Starting Note G on page 2, or
Starting Note C on page 4, or
Group Chords on page 19, or
Five-Note Patterns on page 11.

*
Lip, jaw and throat positions:

Buzzing with the lips:

Buzzing on the mouthpiece:

Long notes:

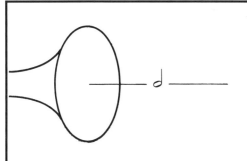

Tongued notes:

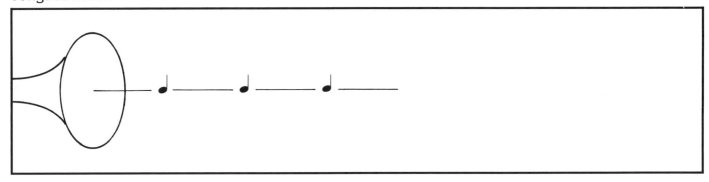

Slurring:

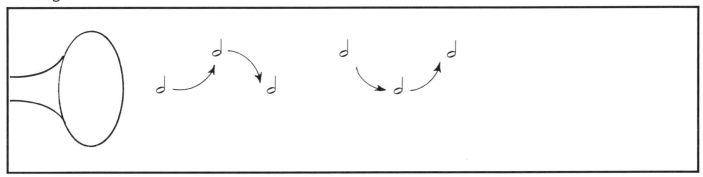

Making up rhythms and melodies, and soundscapes:

All these notes are *possible* on your instrument without using valves, by merely varying the lip-pressure. At first you will probably only be able to produce the lowest notes.

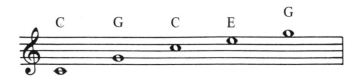

DOUG NOTES

open
(no valves)

Start with G . . .

Clap, say,*
and play
the rhythm

Some of the material on pages 2 and 10 integrates with material on other pages in this and other TEAM BRASS books as an aid to group teaching. Follow indications written above appropriate lines.

The TIME-SIGNATURE 4/4 means each bar must add up to FOUR beats

A CROTCHET (or QUARTER-NOTE) lasts for ONE beat

■ Fits with *F Book* page 4, line 2.

A MINIM (or HALF-NOTE) lasts for TWO beats

■ Fits with *F Book* page 4, line 3.

A CROTCHET REST lasts for ONE beat

A COMMA means take a breath

bar 1   bar 2   bar 3   bar 4

29/9

■ Fits with *F Book* page 4, line 4.

■ Fits with page 10, line 1; with *F Book*, page 4, line 5.

RHYTHM

PULSE — clap or beat time

*French time-names may be used.

. . . then on to F

1st valve

Play the grid across, up or down

BAR LINES divide a line of notes into sets. In $\frac{4}{4}$ time each bar adds up to four crotchet beats

$(2 + 1+1 = 4)$ $(1+1+1+1=4)$

The DOUBLE BAR marks the end of a piece of music

F's and G's

■ Fits with page 5, line 4.

Pavane

Slowly and sadly

■ Proceed down to E, page 6; or up to A, page 17.

or start with C . . .

. . . then on to D

Proceed up to E, on page 7; or down to B, on page 10.

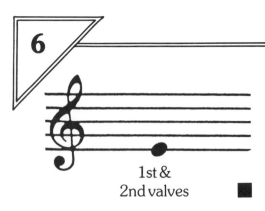

1st &
2nd valves

The note E

■ This page fits harmonically & rhythmically with the one opposite

G, F and E together

A
SEMIBREVE
lasts for
FOUR beats

■ Fits with page 10, line 2; with *F Book* page 1, line 8.

The lost note

All mixed up!

■ This can be played in conjunction with *Acapulco Bay* opposite.

Acapulco Bay

Tempo di Beguine

■ Proceed down to D on page 8; or up to A on page 17

The 'S' symbol means the music can be slurred throughout, if the teacher wishes.

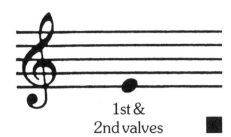

1st &
2nd valves

The note E

■ This page fits harmonically & rhythmically with the one opposite.

C, D and E together

17 th /11/17

The lost note

■ When played in conjunction with *The Lost Note* (opposite) fits with *F Book*, page 1, line 8.

(S)

A SEMIBREVE lasts for FOUR beats

34 ///

Tricky tune!

(S)

1/12 ✶

Acapulco Bay

■ This can be played in conjunction with *Acapulco Bay* opposite.

Tempo di Beguine

■ Proceed up to F on page 9; or down to B on page 10.

The 'S' symbol means the music can be slurred throughout, if the teacher wishes.

G, F, E and D together

G	F	E	D	E	G	D	F	E

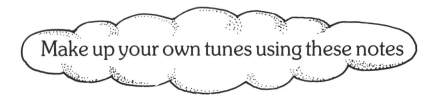

Make up your own tunes using these notes

■ If required, see preparatory 'D' exercises on page 5.

D
(1st and 3rd valves)

■ Fits with page 10, line 4.

Marching

■ Fits with page 10, line 5.   ## Gliding

(S)

Vigorous March   ## Watch your step!

(S)

■ *Watch your step!* can be played in conjunction with *Sort 'em out!* (opposite), or with piano accompaniment.

C, D, E and F together

Make up your own tunes using these notes

■ If required, *see preparatory 'F' exercises on page 3.*

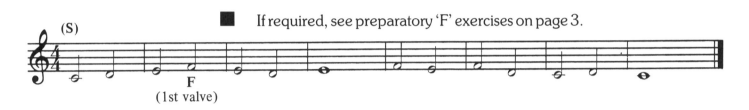

F
(1st valve)

Flowing

Two bar phrase (1) | Two bar phrase (2) | Two bar phrase (3) | Two bar phrase (4)

Walking

Composed by eleven-year old JENNY WONG

Sort 'em out!

March

■ *Sort 'em out!* can be played in conjunction with *Watch your step!* (opposite).

The note low B

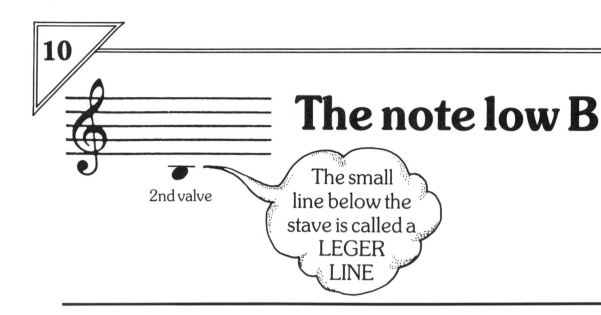

2nd valve

The small line below the stave is called a LEGER LINE

■ All the material on this page integrates with material on previous pages, as marked.

■ Fits with page 2, line 5; with *F Book*, page 4, line 5.

■ Fits with page 6, line 3; with *F Book*, page 1, line 8.

■ Fits with page 6, line 4.

■ Fits with page 8, line 2.

B with C, D and E

■ Fits with page 8, line 4.

■ For related ensemble material see pages 14, 15, 19, 20, 21.

Five-note patterns

Intervals

Step round

play by ear

Welsh tune

Traditional

New Rhythm

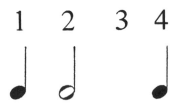

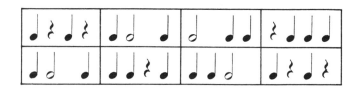

Two rounds

'C' means Common Time i.e. $\frac{4}{4}$ time

Old Liza Jane

Related group 'warm up' on page 19; related ensemble on pages 14 & 15; syncopated ensemble on page 21.

$\frac{3}{4}$ time

Every bar adds up to three crotchets

Slow waltz

Composed by eleven-year old JOANNE AHMED

Four bar question phrase, A

Four bar answer phrase, B

This means 'rest' for 4 whole bars- so count ① 2 3 ② 2 3 ③ 2 3 ④ 2 3 and then play from bar 5

A dotted minim lasts for THREE beats

Gently and dreamily

Les ballons

getting slower

(muted, if possible)

Round lullaby

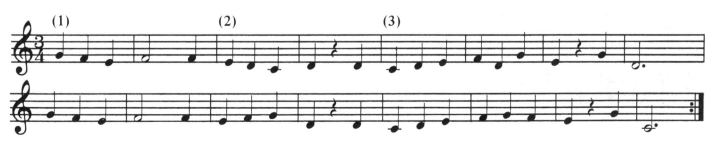

(1) (2) (3)

■ Proceed up to A, page 17; or to quavers, page 22; or F♯, page 24; or low A, page 36.

German tune

Traditional

Duet

Lullaby

Duet

COUNT
① 2 3 ② 2 3

Second and third parts to trumpet duets appear in the *F horn book* and the supplement to the brass band book (treble clef). Fourth parts are in *trombone book* and *supplement*.

Tied notes

A minim tied to a crotchet lasts for 3 beats.

A crotchet tied to a crotchet lasts for 2 beats.

A semibreve tied to a crotchet lasts for 5 beats and so on.

Don't be late!

Canzonetta

Compose a part for tambour or tambourine

More tied notes on pages 18, 20 and 21. Preparatory rounds on pages 11 & 12.

	Valves
1	Open
2	2nd
3	1st
4	1st & 2nd
5	2nd & 3rd

Slurs (1)
and legato tonguing

Play all slurs on different valve combinations

Valve slur/legato tonguing

Proceed up to A; or to 'quavers' on page 22; or to F♯ on page 24; or to low A on page 36.

The note A

1st and
2nd valves

play these notes using varied rhythm patterns

F	A	D
A	C	E
D	A	D
E	G	G

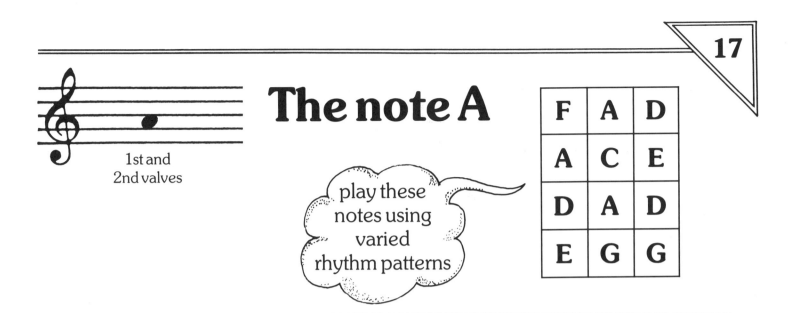

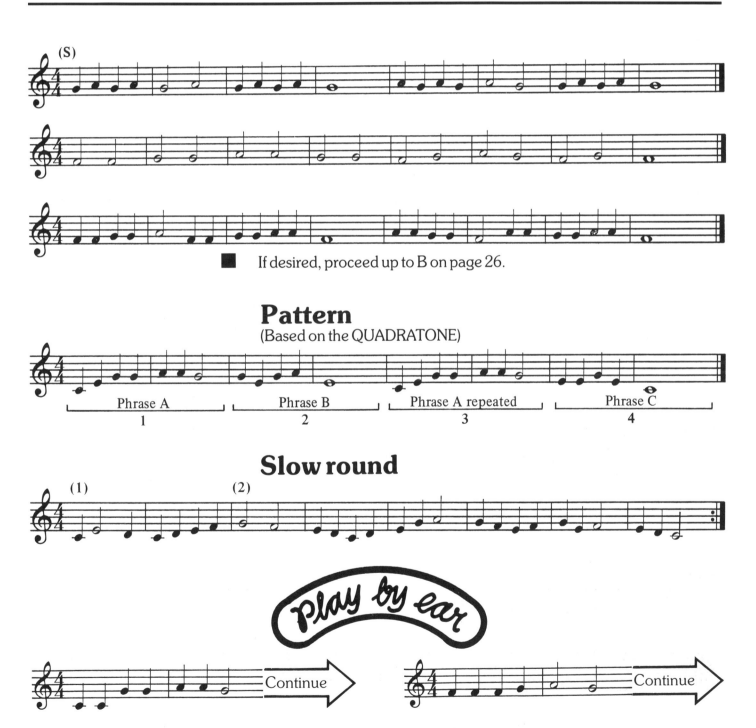

■ If desired, proceed up to B on page 26.

Pattern
(Based on the QUADRATONE)

Phrase A	Phrase B	Phrase A repeated	Phrase C
1	2	3	4

Slow round

(1)　　　(2)

play by ear

Continue　　　Continue

■ *see Accompaniments Book* concerning the QUADRATONE.

New rhythms

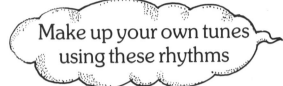

Make up your own tunes using these rhythms

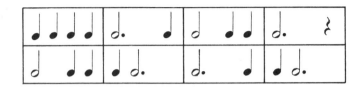

(1) (2) (3)

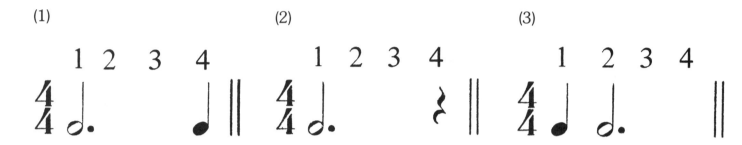

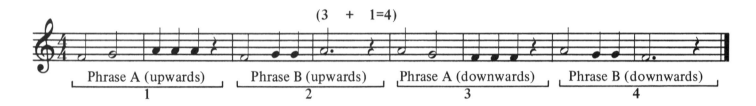

Phrase A (upwards) 1 | Phrase B (upwards) 2 | Phrase A (downwards) 3 | Phrase B (downwards) 4

Stepping out

Strident and fast

When the saints go marching in

Traditional

Bouncy

Proceed to Low A, page 36; or up to B on page 26; or to B♭ on page 32; or to Quavers on page 22; or to F♯ on page 24. Related ensemble on pages 20 & 21.

Brass group warm-up 1

is the sign for PAUSE, meaning the note should be held beyond its normal value

Harmony long notes

(Optional 3rd part)

Practise tonguing on each note, devising your own rhythm patterns

Low G is played with 1st & 3rd valves

Unison long notes

Slurred slow notes

Slurred fast notes

Regal fanfare

Maestoso

*Fanfare part for timpani (or bass drum and tenor drum) and cymbals.

¢ means TWO MINIM BEATS in each bar, ie ²⁄₂ time. (Sometimes called ALLA BREVE time)

When used in conjunction with lower brass and horn, play fanfare twice through: (1) trumpets and timpani; (2) trumpets, lower brass, timpani and cymbals.

When I first came to this land

Traditional

Fast and furious

When three trumpeters are sharing a lesson, the third part for these ensemble pieces is to be found in the *Brass Band Book*.

Blowin' in the wind

On the repeat, omit these bars and go straight to the bar marked 2

Accompaniment for synthesizer on 'samba' rhythm setting

Play three times, then on to 'chorus'

4/4	Bb	Eb	F	Bb	Bb	Eb	F	F7

Chorus

Eb	F	Bb	Gmin	Eb	F	Bb	Bb

Quavers in 4/4 time

Two QUAVERS ♪♪ or ♫ add up to one crotchet

Every bar adds up to four crotchets

(1 + 1 + 2 = 4)

Here we go!

Words and music by
eleven-year old JOANNE O'NEILL

1
Phrase A

2
Phrase B

Here we go, Run-ning in the snow, Hav-ing lots of fun now the Win-ter's just be-gun.

3
Phrase A repeated (same word rhythms)

4
Phrase C

Once a year Comes the fes-tive cheer: Mer - ry Christ - mas and Hap-py New Year!

play by ear

Make up a song about Winter, Spring, Summer or Autumn, using quavers

Continue

Continue

■ Syncopated quavers on page 44; quavers in 6/8 on page 41; dotted-crotchet-quaver on page 42; related ensemble on pages 20, 37 & 49.

Quavers in $\frac{3}{4}$ & $\frac{2}{4}$ time

■ $\frac{2}{4}$ Rhythm Grid on page 34.

(2 + 1=3)

Roundabout

(1)   (2)   (3)   (4)

This means
'rest' for 2 whole bars
so count ①2, ② 2
and then play from bar 3

Make up your own
tune about something
that moves quickly
using quavers

Sleigh ride

Fast

loud

fairly loud

very loud

The note F sharp

A	E	F♯	A	E
F	G	D	F♯	F

2nd valve

The SHARP raises the pitch of a note by one semitone

Play these notes using varied rhythm patterns

Compose your own piece about a bird or animal – or one of the seasons

The cuckoo

Composed by ten-year old EDWARD DUCKETT

Cuckoo returns in spring . . . .

(loud)

Fine

. . . . and departs in autumn . . . .

(soft)

D.C. al Fine

Watch out for F's which are not sharpened

This stands for DA CAPO AL FINE, which means go back to the beginning and finish at the bar marked FINE

Play by ear

Continue

Continue

Key-signature

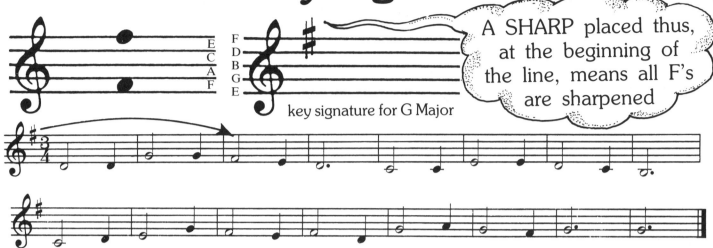

key signature for G Major

A SHARP placed thus, at the beginning of the line, means all F's are sharpened

Slavic slurs

Smoothly

■ To be played with *legato tonguing* or *slurring* throughout, as directed.

F sharps & quavers

Austrian Holiday

F/F♯ Study

Lilting

(Accent)

Fine *slower*

D.C. al Fine
a tempo

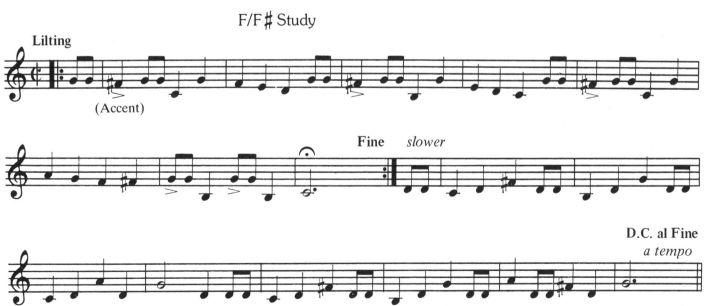

■ Related ensemble on page 37.

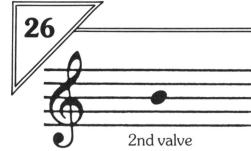

The note B

2nd valve

Sing hosanna

Merrily

Traditional

Victorian ballad

In relaxed style

Fine

D.C. al Fine

This stands for DA CAPO AL FINE, which means go back to the beginning and end at the bar marked FINE

■ B flat (page 32) can be introduced before B, if desired.

Workin' on the railroad

Traditional

Like a jolly cowboy saloon song

5/4 time

Waiting!

Relevant ensemble: B with quavers, page 37.

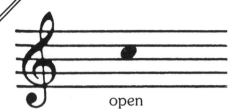

Upper C

open

Scale and arpeggio of C

C chromatic scale

Intervals

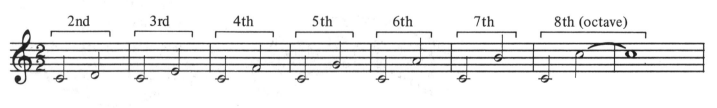

Look for scale patterns

Round the scale

You will find a GLOSSARY of musical terms on page 62

Study in C

play by ear

Try playing by ear, your favourites from the world of classics, pop or TV.

Slurs (2)
And valve slurs/legato tonguing

	Valves
1	Open
2	2nd
3	1st
4	1st & 2nd
5	2nd & 3rd
6	1st & 3rd
7	1st, 2nd & 3rd

■ Delete anacrusis as necessary.

Play all slurs on different valve combinations

Valve slur/legato tonguing

The FLAT lowers the pitch of a note by one semitone (see page 32)

Relaxation

* Upper D on page 35

Plainchant

Refer to the CHROMATIC SCALE (page 28) for any notes you don't already know

My favourite things

From *The Sound of Music*

Words by OSCAR HAMMERSTEIN II
Music by RICHARD RODGERS

■ Chromatic scale on page 28. Proceed up to D, page 35; or down
to A, page 36; or to B♭, page 32; or to quavers, page 34.

32

The note B flat

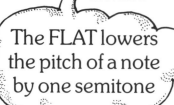

The FLAT lowers the pitch of a note by one semitone

1st valve

F	G	A	B♭	E	A	F
C	B♭	D	G	F	C	E

D minor round

We wish you a Merry Christmas Traditional

Fast and jolly

Play by ear

Continue

Continue

■ Related ensemble, page 49; F scale, page 52; D minor scale, pages 58 & 59.

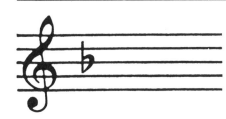

Key-signature of F major D minor

Yankee Doodle

Traditional

Aura Lee

Traditional

The natural sign

2nd valve

The NATURAL cancels the effect of a flat (or a sharp)

F major round

Coventry carol

Traditional

*Upper D on page 35.

Quavers up to C

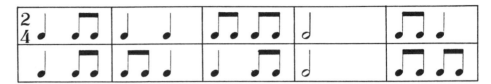

Quaver study

Allegro

Syncopated quavers on page 44; semiquavers on page 40; dotted crotchet on page 42; $\frac{6}{8}$ quavers on page 41; dotted quavers on page 50.

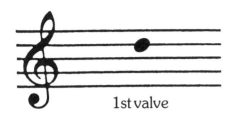

Upper D

1st valve

Limp round

(1)   (2)   (3)

Edelweiss
From *The Sound of Music*

words by OSCAR HAMMERSTEIN II
music by RICHARD RODGERS

Semplice

mp

f

rall...

---

play by ear

Continue ➡

Continue ➡

■ 6/8 up to D, page 39; quavers up to D, pages 39, 45; semiquavers up to D, page 40. D major key on page 47. Relaxation exercises on page 30. Dotted-crotchet/quaver, page 42.

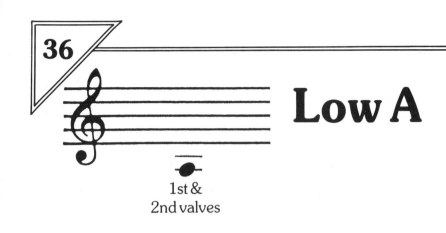

Low A

1st &
2nd valves

(S)

Quadratone pattern

Compose your own piece using the notes of the QUADRATONE*

Low round

(1)   (2)

mp

🎹 Theme from Polovtsian dances

ALEXANDER BORODIN (1833-87)

Lilting, not fast

mp (mf)

■ Related ensemble on pages 37 and 48.
*A useful group of notes requiring open and 1/2 fingering only.

Au clair de la lune

Traditional

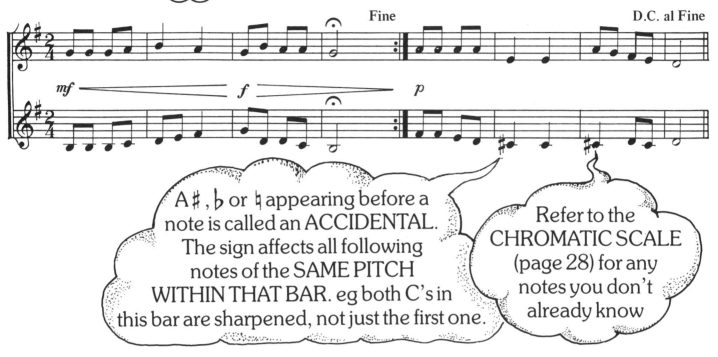

> A ♯, ♭ or ♮ appearing before a note is called an ACCIDENTAL. The sign affects all following notes of the SAME PITCH WITHIN THAT BAR. eg both C's in this bar are sharpened, not just the first one.

> Refer to the CHROMATIC SCALE (page 28) for any notes you don't already know

Little donkey

words and music by ERIC BOSWELL

Preparatory C♯ exercises on page 47.

Brass group warm-up 2

Harmony long notes

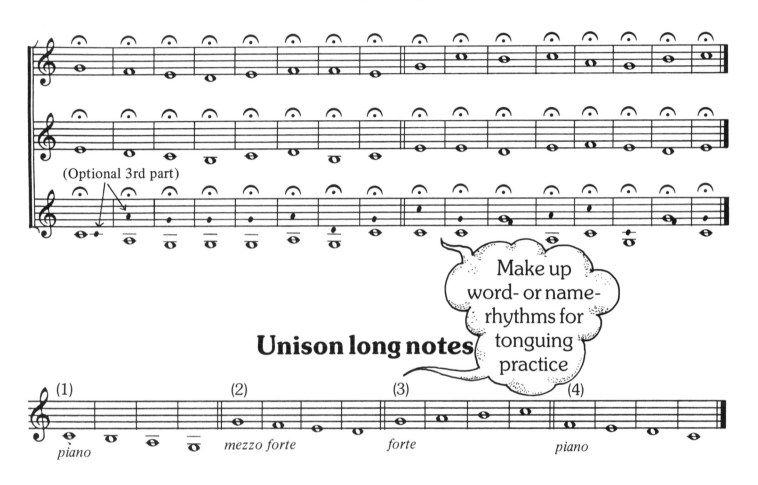

(Optional 3rd part)

Make up word- or name-rhythms for tonguing practice

Unison long notes

(1) piano   (2) mezzo forte   (3) forte   (4) piano

Scale exercise

piano   crescendo   forte   diminuendo   piano   *p* — *f* — *p* — *f*

Slurs

(1)

(2)

■ more level (2) slurs on page 30.

Tijuana brass

 I saw three ships

Traditional

Semiquavers in $\frac{2}{4}$

Semiquaver study

Join the dots in order to make 'ties' as and when required

Related ensemble on pages 48 and 55.

$\frac{6}{8}$ time

The dotted crotchet in $\frac{4}{4}$

Make up your own melodies using dotted rhythms

Join the dots to make the dotted-crotchet/ quaver effect

Theme
from *"New World"* Symphony

ANTONIN DVOŘÁK
(1841-1904)

Quick march

Composed by nine-year old
REBECKA ELEY

'Ode to joy'

LUDWIG VAN BEETHOVEN
(1770-1827)

Allegro assai

Play by ear

Related ensemble on pages 48 and 49.

The dotted crotchet in $\frac{3}{4}$ and $\frac{2}{4}$

Compose your own piece about an interesting place or far-away country

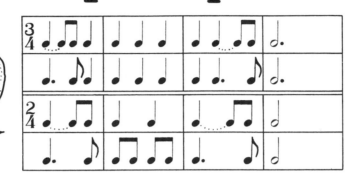

Scottish ballad

Legato e cantabile

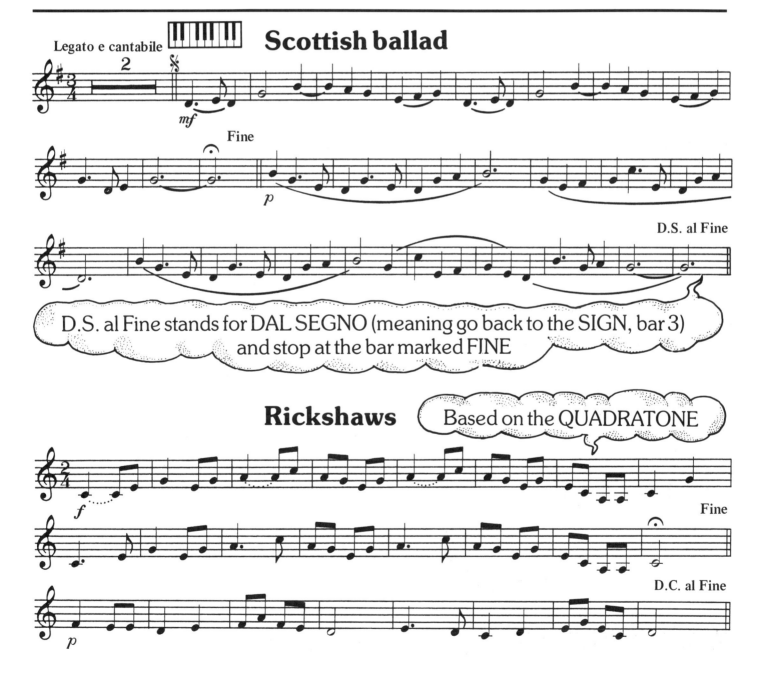

D.S. al Fine stands for DAL SEGNO (meaning go back to the SIGN, bar 3) and stop at the bar marked FINE

Rickshaws

Based on the QUADRATONE

See *Accompaniments Book* concerning the QUADRATONE.

Quaver syncopation

To be played (A) in strict time and (B) in swinging time

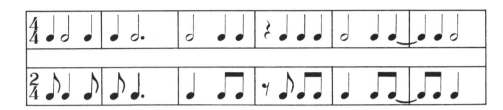

Old Liza Jane

See Glossary for new signs

Caribbean dance

Traditional

Tempo di Rumba

Fine

D.C. al Fine

Continue

■ Syncopated crotchets on pages 12, 15 and 21; Related ensemble on page 39. *Upper E on page 50.

Simply blue

Twelve bar blues

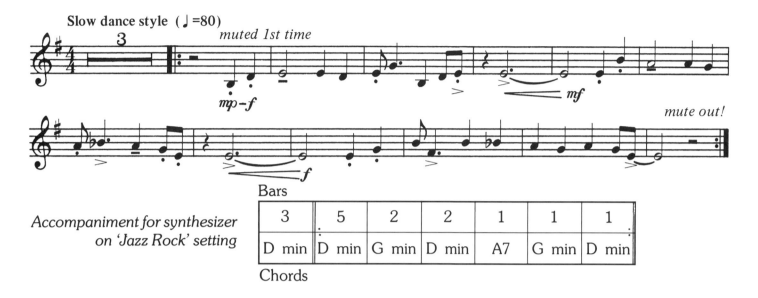

Slow dance style (♩=80)

muted 1st time

mute out!

Accompaniment for synthesizer
on 'Jazz Rock' setting

Bars						
3	5	2	2	1	1	1
D min	D min	G min	D min	A7	G min	D min

Chords

West Indian carnival

Very fast and rhythmic

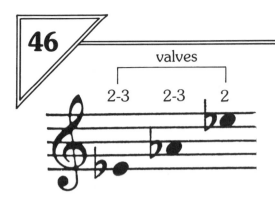

valves

2-3   2-3   2

The notes A flat and E flat

Key-signature of E♭ major

Villikins and his Dinah

Traditional

mp

f *mf* *p*

The swinger

Twelve bar blues

Swinging style (♩ =132)

f

Pattern 1   Pattern 2

ff   Pattern 3   *mf*

Suggested variation

(ossia)

mf   *f*

ff   *mp*   *ff*

Accompaniment for synthesizer on '16 beat' rhythm setting

Bars					
4	2	2	1	1	2
E♭ min	A♭ min	E♭ min	B♭ 7	A♭ min	E♭ min

Chords   (B♭7 ♭13)

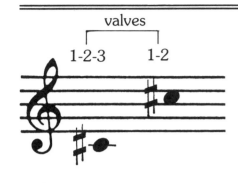

The note C sharp
Key-signature of D major

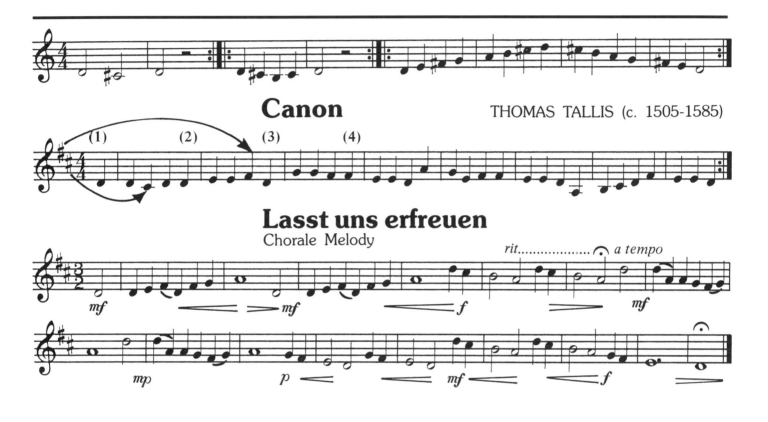

Canon
THOMAS TALLIS (c. 1505-1585)

Lasst uns erfreuen
Chorale Melody

L.A. Nitespot
Twelve bar blues

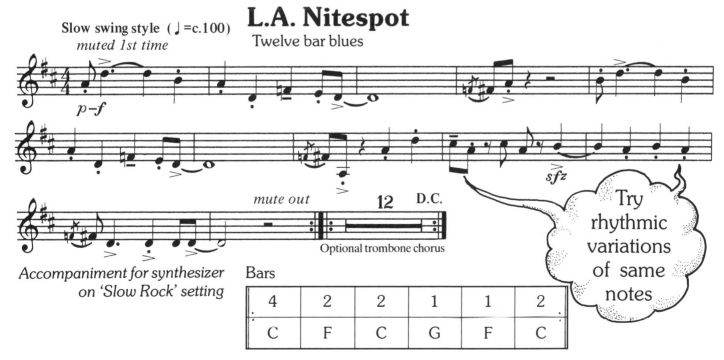

Optional trombone chorus

Accompaniment for synthesizer on 'Slow Rock' setting

Try rhythmic variations of same notes

Bars					
4	2	2	1	1	2
C	F	C	G	F	C

Chords

■ Scale of D minor on page 58.

Because the CANZONA is a four-part polyphonic piece, the parts above cannot be played simply as a trumpet duet. Third and fourth parts are to be found in all other *Team Brass* books.

O Little Town of Bethlehem

Traditional

St. Anthony chorale

JOSEPH HAYDN (1732-1809)

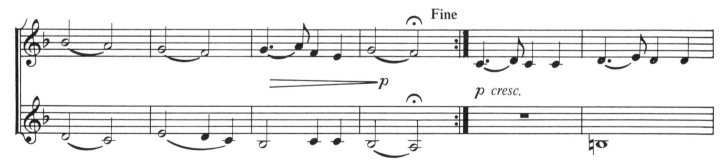

open

Upper E

ossia

I gave my love a cherry

Traditional

The dotted quaver

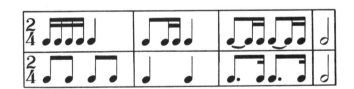

Theme

Canon

Gustav Mahler (1860-1911)

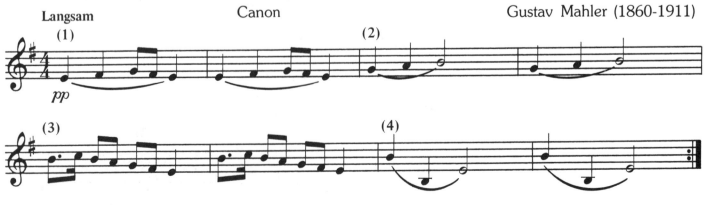

■ 'Relaxation' exercises on page 30.

Say 'goodbye'

From the opera *Marriage of Figaro*

WOLFGANG AMADEUS MOZART (1756-1791)

Triplet quaver group - Three quavers played in the time of one crotchet

Old Spanish town

Extra material up to E on pages 44, 48, 49, 54, 58 and 59.

Upper F

1st valve

Scale & arpeggio of F

The first noel

Traditional

The centipede's masterpiece

composed by fifteen-year old SARAH HART

Jolly

mf

cresc.

f dim.

mf cresc.

ff

mf

f

pp

'Relaxation exercises' on page 30.

Pomp and circumstance

EDWARD ELGAR (1857-1934)

Gallop

from the opera *Orpheus in the Underworld*

JACQUES OFFENBACH (1819-1880)

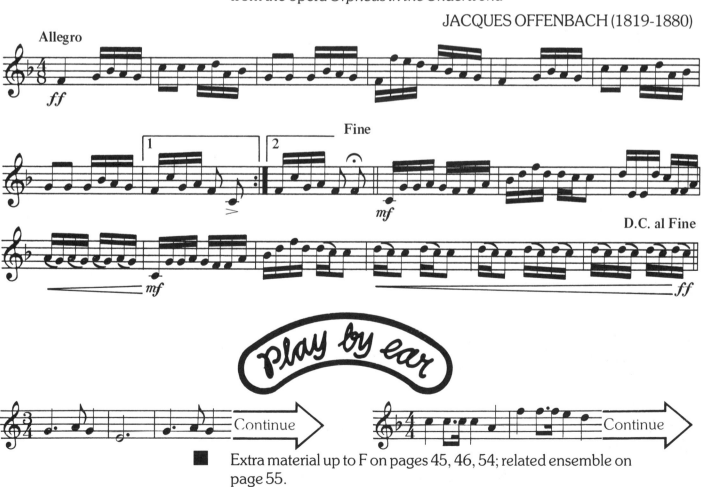

Extra material up to F on pages 45, 46, 54; related ensemble on page 55.

Slurs (3)

Intervals

(slurred and tongued)

Chromatic scale

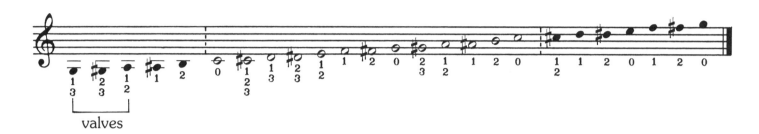

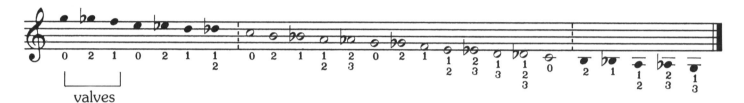

March

from *Judas Maccabaeus*

GEORGE FRIDERIC HANDEL (1685-1759)

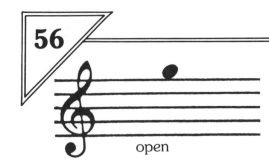

Upper G

open

Chorale

HANS HASSLER (1564-1612)

Legato e cantabile

mp

mf

p

'Star Wars' Main Title

JOHN WILLIAMS

Allegro assai

f

To Coda

f

mf

D.S. al Coda

f

ff

CODA

ff

fff

D.S. al Coda means repeat the section from 𝄋 to ⊕ and then cut to the CODA section

'Relaxation exercises' on page 30.

Scale of G major

March

from *Occasional Oratorio*

GEORGE FRIDERIC HANDEL (1685-1759)

'Running' scale of G

Extra material up to G on pages 56, 60 and 61.

Scales and arpeggios

A minor harmonic

A minor melodic

Arpeggio of A minor

D minor harmonic

■ D major on page 47

D minor melodic

E major

■ E flat major, page 46

E minor harmonic

E minor melodic

C major

Arpeggio of C major

B♭ major

Arpeggio of B♭ major

Slurs (4)

■ 'Relaxation exercises' on page 30.

Grand finale

Printed and bound in Great Britain by Caligraving Limited

Glossary of musical terms

MUSICAL TERM	ABBREVIATION	MEANING IN ENGLISH
forte	_f_	loudly
mezzoforte	_mf_	(lit. half) moderately loud
piano	_p_	softly
mezzopiano	_mp_	(lit. half) moderately softly
fortissimo	_ff_	very loudly
pianissimo	_pp_	very softly
crescendo	_cresc._ or ◁	getting louder
diminuendo	_dim._ or ▷	getting quieter
ritenuto/ritardando	_rit._	getting slower
a tempo		at the original speed
tempo		speed
subito	_sub._	suddenly
Moderato		at a moderate speed
Allegro		merry, quick, bright
Grandioso		grandly
Con brio		with spirit
simile	_sim._	Continue playing in same style
Langsam		slowly
Da Capo (Al fine)	D.C. or D.C. al Fine	Go back to the beginning (and stop at the place marked Fine)
Presto		quickly
staccato		detached, ie, the opposite of Legato
tenuto		Hold for full value
rallentando	_rall._	gradually slowing down
Religioso		religiously
Semplice		simply
Andante		at walking pace
Maestoso		majestically
Adagio		slowly
piano-(forte)	_p(f)_	Play quietly first time, and loudly when music is repeated
Common time	C	$\frac{4}{4}$ ie four crotchets per bar
Alla Breve	¢	$\frac{2}{2}$ ie two minim beats per bar
Dal Segno	D. 𝄋 (al Coda)	Go back to the 'sign' (and then go to Coda')
Assai		very
Legato		smoothly
Cantabile		in a singing style
Et / E }		and
Ossia		alternative